Name _____

Write

grab   people   sna...
nice   small   wa...

The pets have a car __wash__ .

1. A __snake__ comes.

2. Some __people__ come too.

3. They look very __nice__ .

4. This car is __small__ .

5. The dog will __grab__ a rag and wash it.

Directions: Use some words from the story "Pet Wash" to complete these sentences. Read the sentence in the sample. Read the words in bold print at the top of the page. Write the word that belongs in the sentence. Read the sentence again to check your word.

Have pupils draw lines around all the words that name animals. Then have them draw lines under all the words that name things.

"Pet Wash" and "My Very Own Pet," pages 4–15
Vocabulary: key words

1

Name _____

The friends had a pet wash.
The friends read a book.

1. A dog and a snake came to the wash.

A snake and a pig ran out.

2. The cat had a funny hat.
The cat ran out.

3. Kate said, "Grab that snake!"
Kate will pat the head of the dog.

4. The pet wash was a people wash.
A nice horse came to the pet wash.

Directions: This page tells about the story "Pet Wash." Look at the picture in the sample. It shows characters from the story. Read the two sentences. Draw a line under the sentence that tells about the characters. Do the rest of the page the same way.

 Have pupils write a sentence about one of the pets at the pet wash. Then they may draw a picture to go with the sentence.

Name _____

It is nice at the  .

land   pond

1. Meg has fun on the  .

stand   sand

2. Meg can do a hand  .

send   stand

3. Now and then the  is cold.

band   wind

4. Cold hands and toes _____ Meg home.

send   land

Directions: Some words end with the consonant sounds of **nd,** as in **band.** Read the sentence in the sample. Read the two words in bold print. They both end with the **nd** sound. Write the word that belongs in the sentence. Read the sentence again to check your word.

 Have pupils use words that end in **nd.**

"Pet Wash" and "My Very Own Pet," pages 4–15
Decoding: <u>nd</u> (hand)

pig

pig   peg

1.

pan

pan

pin   pan

2.

wig

wig

wig   wag

3.

bug

bug

bug   big

4.

nut

nut

not   nut

5.

ten

ten

ten   tan

6.

dog

dog

dog   dig

7.

mat

mat

met   mat

8.

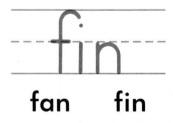

fin

fin

fan   fin

Directions: Some words have short vowel sounds: **a** as in **cat, e** as in **ten, i** as in **pig, o** as in **top,** and **u** as in **bug.**
Look at the sample. Say the name of the picture. Read the two words in bold print. Write the word that names the picture.
Do the rest of the page the same way.

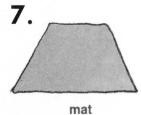 Have pupils add different vowels to finish words: **c–p, h–t, t–p.** Have them write the words they make.

4

"**Pet Wash**" **and** "**My Very Own Pet**," **pages 4–15**
Decoding: short vowels a, e, i, o, u

Rex said, "Mom, will you dance with me?"
"I can not dance with you now," said Mom.
Rex was not happy.

"Who will dance with me?"
he said.

"I will," said the fox.

 Write

Mom did not dance. Rex was  sad .

happy   sad

1. The fox said, "I will." Rex was happy .

happy   sad

2. The fox is kind .

kind   bad

Directions: Characters in stories may be people or animals. Stories tell how characters look, feel, and act. Read the story about Rex. Read the sentence in the sample. Read the two words in bold print. Write the word that tells about Rex.

 Have pupils suggest a different ending to the story. What might have happened if Rex had not found anyone to dance with him?

"Pet Wash" and "My Very Own Pet," pages 4–15
Comprehension: character traits

The dogs have a new ____ .

○ help   ● house

1. The house is for 2 ____ of dogs.
   ● kinds   ○ kids

2. ____ dogs can be big or small.
   ○ That   ● These

3. There are ____ kinds of dogs.
   ○ most   ● many

4. They are all ____ by the house.
   ● there   ○ these

5. ____ dogs will fit in the house?
   ● Which   ○ Who

Directions: Use some words from the story "All Kinds of Pets" to complete these sentences. Read the sentence in the sample. Read the two words in bold print. Fill in the circle beside the word that belongs in the sentence. Read the sentence again to check your word.

 Have pupils write their answer to the question at the end of the story.

6   "All Kinds of Pets," pages 16–19
Vocabulary: key words

Name _____

Check	Big	Small	In	Out
puppy		✔	✔	✔
1. horse	✔			✔
2. parakeet		✔	✔	
3. duck		✔		✔
4. rabbit		✔		✔
5. sheep	✔			✔

Directions: This page tells about the story "All Kinds of Pets." Look at the sample. Read the words at the top. They tell about pets. Some pets are big; others are small. Some pets stay in the house; others stay out of the house. Look at the picture in the sample. Put a check in all the boxes that tell about this pet. Do the rest of the page the same way.

Have pupils decide which pet they would most like to have. Have them draw a picture of themselves and that pet, showing what they would do together.

Is this a big knot? **yes**

Did he sit on a rock? **no**

1. Did she knit it? **yes**

2. Did he put on a sock? **yes**

3. Will she knock? **yes**

4. Can the bird pick it up? **no**

Directions: Some words end with the consonant **ck** sound, as in **back.** Some words begin with the consonant **kn** sound, as in **know.** Each question on this page has a word with **ck** or **kn.** Look at the first picture in the sample. Read the question about the picture. Write **yes** or **no** to answer the question. Do the rest of the page the same way.

 Have pupils use the letters **ck** and **kn** to complete these words: **si–, pa–, bri–; –ow, –ee, —ife.**

8   "All Kinds of Pets," pages 16–19
Decoding: <u>ck</u> (duck), <u>kn</u> (knife)

Cross out

Name _____

rooster   goose   frog

1.

kitten   cow   horse

2.

 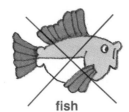 

goat   fish   sheep

3.

parakeet   eagle   rabbit

4.

 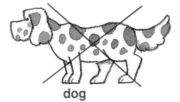 

snake   dog   lizard

Directions: Some animals are alike and some are different. For example, a kitten and a hamster are small, but a horse and an elephant are big. Look at the first row of pictures. Think about which animals are alike and which are different. Then put an **X** on the picture of the animal that does not belong with the others.

 Have pupils tell why the animals in each row are the same or different.

"All Kinds of Pets," pages 16–19
Vocabulary: classification

9

Many people like hats. Hats help people stay warm. Hats help people look nice.

What is the story about?

Hats Can Help You Stay Warm

Why People Like Hats

---

1. You can help at home. You can bake a cake. You can bring in the paper.

What is the story about?

Ways You Can Help At Home

What People Do at Home

---

2. Beth has many balloons. She has big and small balloons. Some balloons look like a duck and a pig.

What is the story about?

A Duck and A Pig

Lots of Balloons

Directions: The main idea of a story is the most important thing it tells. Sometimes a title tells what the story is about. Read the story in the sample. Read the two titles. Draw a line under the title that tells what the story is about. Do the rest of the page the same way.

 Have pupils choose one of the stories and write a different title for it. Have pupils share their titles and see if each one fits the story.

"All Kinds of Pets," pages 16–19
Comprehension: main idea

asked   does   play   star

boy   name   Shall

Write

My __name__ is Max.

You can see by my name that I am a __boy__ .

I am in a __play__ ! I am a __star__ .

My class __asked__ me to be the pig.

The pig __does__ not say much. But he is big!

__Shall__ I be the pig?

Directions: Use some words from the story "The Play" to complete these sentences. Read the sentence in the sample. Read the words in bold print at the top of the page. Write the word that belongs in the sentence. Read the sentence again to check your word.

 Have pupils answer the question at the end of the story and discuss their reasons.

Name _____

| 1 | Mrs. Fine said, "Class, let's put on a play." |

| 4 | Mrs. Fine said, "What will I do?" |

| 5 | The class put on a new play, *Seven Snow Whites and the Dwarf.* |

| 2 | Many people want to be Snow White. |

| 3 | Max wants to be the dwarf in the play. |

Directions: This page tells about the story "The Play." Read the sentence in the sample. This is what happened first in the story. Put a **1** in the box. Now read the other sentences. Number them **2, 3, 4, 5** in order to show what happened in the story.

 Have pupils write a sentence that tells what they think happened when the play was over and put a **6** in front of it.

"The Play," pages 20–25
Selection Comprehension

A big plow •　　　• has a hat.

The snowman •　　　• can push the snow.

1. Greg •　　　• is good to eat.

2. This snack •　　　• has a big grin.

3. I play •———————• on the grass.

4. The snail •———————• is in a play.

5. My snake •　　　• is on the plate.

6. A plum •　　　• is a good pet.

Directions: Some words begin with the consonant sounds of **pl** as in **plan, sn** as in **snail,** and **gr** as in **grin.** Look at the picture in the sample. Read the sentence beginnings and endings. Draw a line from each sentence beginning to the correct sentence ending. Read both sentences again to check your work. Do the rest of the page the same way.

 Have pupils use their books to find and list words beginning with pl, sn, and gr.

"The Play," pages 20–25
Decoding: pl (plant), sn (snake), gr (green)

Name _____

	It's Something to Eat	It Can Sleep	It's in the House	It's for Your Hands
Check — mittens			✔	✔
1. parakeet		✔	✔	
2. apple	✔		✔	
3. stove			✔	
4. ring			✔	✔
5. cherries	✔		✔	

Directions: The chart on this page shows how some things are alike and how they are different. Read the categories across the top. Look at the first picture. Put a check in each box that tells about the picture. Do the rest of the page the same way.

 Have pupils name something else that belongs in each group on this page and draw a picture. Then have pupils share pictures and identify categories.

"The Play," pages 20–25
Vocabulary: classification

Draw a line under

Jim has a pet rabbit.
<u>The rabbit reads funny books.</u>

1. <u>The cat said, "Hello, you are my friend."</u>
   Jan said, "Hello, you are my friend."

2. <u>Tom's dog can bake a cake.</u>
   Tom and his dad can bake a cake.

3. Some birds are blue and fly.
   <u>The red bird can fly to the stars.</u>

4. <u>A cow can jump over the moon.</u>
   A cow can stand or sit and eat.

5. This is a fine, fat frog.
   <u>The frog will dance for you.</u>

Directions: Some stories are about things that could really happen. Other stories are make-believe. Look at the picture. Read the sentences in the sample. Draw a line under the sentence that could **not** really happen. Do the rest of the page the same way.

 Have pupils change the sentences they underlined to tell something that could really happen.

"The Play," pages 20–25
Comprehension: reality–fantasy

cook   Kate's   pizza

cooking   lunch   soon

I like to ___cook___ good things.

1. Kate will come home for ___lunch___ today.

2. I will make ___pizza___ for Kate.

3. ___Kate's___ pizza is too hot now.

4. But ___soon___ she can eat it.

5. I like ___cooking___ for Kate too!

Directions: Use some words from the story "Lunch at Kate's" to complete these sentences. Read the sentence in the sample. Read the words in bold print at the top of the page. Write the word that belongs in the sentence. Read the sentence again to check your word.

 Have pupils draw a circle around every word that has something to do with food.

16   "Lunch at Kate's," pages 26–32
         Vocabulary: key words

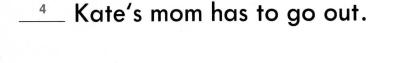
__1__ Kate asks Kim to come for lunch.

__5__ The friends have pizza for lunch.

__4__ Kate's mom has to go out.

__3__ Kate asks Rob and Max too.

__2__ Kim asks her mom if she can go.

Directions: This page tells about the story "Lunch at Kate's." Read the sentence in the sample. This happened first in the story. Put a **1** on the line. Now read the rest of the sentences. Number them **2,3,4,5** to tell what happened in the story.

 Have pupils write a sentence telling what they like to eat when they invite a friend to lunch. They can draw a picture to go with the sentence.

"Lunch at Kate's," pages 26–32
Selection Comprehension

17

Don said, "Dad will get some **chicks** ."

chicks   **chat**

1. Dad will pay with a **check** .

check   **chin**

2. They do not cost **much** .

such   **much**

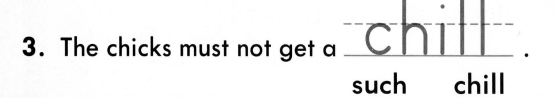

3. The chicks must not get a **chill** .

such   **chill**

4. We will put them in a **chest** to stay warm.

chest   **check**

Directions: Some words have the consonant **ch** sound, as in **chair** and **beach.** Read the sentence in the sample. Read the two words in bold print. They both have the **ch** sound. Write the word that belongs in the sentence. Read the sentence again to check your word.

 Have pupils look through magazines to find three pictures of things that begin with **ch.**
Pupils can make a **ch** bulletin board or chart.

We are **fishing**.

fished   fishing

1. I am **cooking** this lunch.

cooked   cooking

2. My mom is **helping** me.

helped   helping

3. I **asked** Bill to have lunch.

asked   asking

Directions: Sometimes words have **ed** or **ing** at the end. Look at the picture in the sample. Read the sentence and the words in bold print. Write the word that belongs in the sentence. Read the sentence again to check your word.

 Have pupils write their own sentences using one of these word pairs: **played/playing, washed/washing, looked/looking.**

"Lunch at Kate's," pages 26–32
Decoding: inflections **-ed, -ing** (verb)

Name _____

The cat has a hat.

It is the **cat's** hat.

1. The hen has a pen.

It is the **hen's** pen.

2. The fox has a box.

It is the **fox's** box.

3. The pig has a wig.

It is the **pig's** wig.

4. The rat has a bat.

It is the **rat's** bat.

Directions: An **apostrophe** and **s** are added to show that something belongs to someone. Look at the sample and read the first sentence. Think about who owns something. Write the word that belongs in the second sentence. Do the rest of the page the same way.

Have pupils write these pairs of sentences, filling in the blanks: **Peg has a** _____ **. It is** _____
_____ **. Bob has a** _____ **. It is** _____ _____ **.**

"Lunch at Kate's," pages 26–32
Decoding: possessives -'s

Number

2

She sees a puppy at a shop.

1

She takes the puppy home.

3

---

1. He is ready to go out.

2

1

He plays in the snow.

3

2.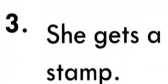

3

The boy is eating.

2

The boy can make things to eat.

1

3. She gets a stamp.

2

She puts "Hello, Max" on some paper.

1

3

Directions: As you read a story think about the order in which things happen. Look at the picture and the sentences in the sample. Number them in the order in which things happen. Do the rest of the page the same way.

 Have pupils name three things they do when they are getting ready to go to bed. Ask them to think of what they do first, second, and third and draw pictures showing the order.

"Lunch at Kate's," pages 26–32
Comprehension: sequence

21

We are ____ to make pizza.
- ● going   ○ go

1. The ____ will help.
- ● teacher   ○ them

2. She will tell us ____ we do a good job.
- ○ it   ● if

3. Do steps 4, 5, and 6 ____ the pizza will not be good.
- ● or   ○ off

4. Make the pizza and cook it till it is ____.
- ○ not   ● hot

5. Take it out ____ the bell rings.
- ○ who   ● when

6. Then eat ____!
- ○ going   ● everything

Directions: Use some words from the story "Lunch With Your Friends" to complete these sentences. Read the sentence in the sample. Read the two words in bold print. Fill in the circle beside the word that belongs in the sentence. Read the sentence again to check your word.

 Make a recipe for pizza with the class. Have the pupils suggest the steps in the process. Write the steps on the board. Have pupils write the recipe and take it home.

"Lunch With Your Friends," pages 33–37
Vocabulary: key words

Can friends help make pizza? __yes__

1. Will you ask a friend to help? __yes__

2. Will you wash your hands? __yes__

3. Will you get everything ready? __no__

4. Will you put a balloon on your pizza? __no__

5. Will you eat the pizza if it is too hot? __no__

Directions: This page is about the story "Lunch With Your Friends." Read the question in the sample and think about the story. Write **yes** or **no** to answer the question. Do the rest of the page the same way.

 Have pupils discuss what they can make for lunch. Have them draw a picture showing how they make that food and write this sentence under the picture: **I can make _____ for lunch.**

"Lunch With Your Friends," pages 33–37
Selection Comprehension

She will play ball.

She will __kick__ it.

trick   kick

1.

He does not feel well.

He is __sick__ .

sock   sick

2.

She can fly a kite.

She made a __knot__ .

knit   knot

3.

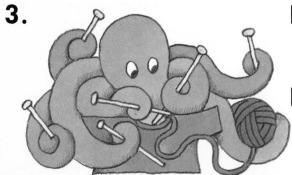

He will make something for you.

He will __knit__ it.

knock   knit

Directions: Some words have the consonant sound of **kn** as in **knob** or **ck** as in **duck.** Look at the picture in the sample. Read the sentences and the words in bold print. Write the word that belongs in the sentence. Read the sentence again to check your word.

 Have pupils choose a **ck** word they did not write. Write a sentence using that word.

"Lunch With Your Friends," pages 33–37
Decoding: <u>ck</u> (duck), <u>kn</u> (knife)

Draw a line around

Name _____

snake

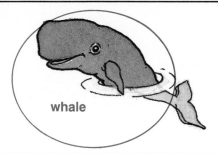
whale

bag

tack

1. cake

rabbit

cane

gate

2. Kate

map

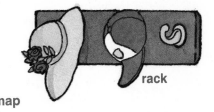
rack

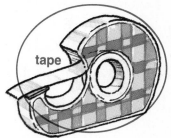
tape

3. name

Nan

rake

skates

4. made

cage

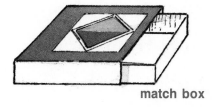
match box

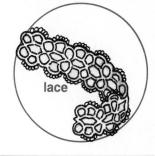
lace

Directions: Some words have a long **a** vowel sound, as in **tape.** Read the word in the sample. Look at the pictures in the row. Draw a line around the pictures whose names have the long **a** sound. There may be more than one picture in each row with the long **a** vowel sound.

 Have pupils write the word that names each picture they circled on the page.

"Lunch With Your Friends," pages 33–37
Decoding: <u>a</u> (cake)

Name _____

You can do many things with paper.
You can paint on paper. You can cut it.
You can fold paper to make cards.
What is the story about?
○ Making Paper Plates
● Making Things with Paper

1. All pets sleep. When you sleep, your dog sleeps. Your cat may sleep when you are playing. Pet birds sleep in cages.
What is the story about?
● Sleep for Pets
○ Sleeping in a Cage

2. Many ducks live at the pond. The ducks have fun. They swim and dive. They look for things to eat.
What is the story about?
○ Food for Ducks
● Ducks at the Pond

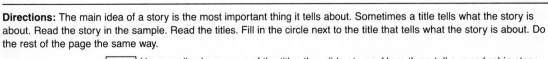

Directions: The main idea of a story is the most important thing it tells about. Sometimes a title tells what the story is about. Read the story in the sample. Read the titles. Fill in the circle next to the title that tells what the story is about. Do the rest of the page the same way.

 Have pupils choose one of the titles they did not use. Have them tell a round-robin story that might have that title, each pupil adding one sentence.

26   "Lunch With Your Friends," pages 33–37
Comprehension: main idea

 **Write**

green   mix   paint   stop   today

Carlos wanted to **paint** the house.

"I will get paint **today**," said Carlos.

"Can we **stop** for pizza?" said Max.

"I just want **green** paint," said Carlos.

"You can **mix** blue paint and yellow paint," said Max.

"Good!" said Carlos. Then they got some pizza.

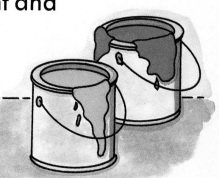

Directions: Use some words from the story "Look Out!" to complete these sentences. Read the sentence in the sample. Read the words in bold print at the top of the page. Write the word that belongs in the sentence. Read the sentence again to check your word.

 Have pupils write one sentence using the words **green** and **paint**. They can draw a picture to go with their sentence.

Name _____

Kate •   • said, "Today we are all going to paint."

Mrs. Fine •   • did not like what the cat and the dog did.

1. Carlos • ——————— • said "We ran out of green paint."

2. Mrs. Fine • ——— • liked what the cat did.

3. Kate •   • spilled the paint.

4. The cat and dog •   • said that blue and yellow paint make green paint.

Directions: This page is about the story "Look Out!" Look at the sample and read the names of the characters. Then read the sentences that tell about the characters. Draw a line from the characters' names to the words that tell what they did in the story. Do the rest of the page the same way.

Have pupils think about how the dog and cat made a painting. Ask what they think the painting looked like. Have them write two sentences about the painting and draw a picture to go with them.

"Look Out!" pages 38–42
Selection Comprehension

You can use this.

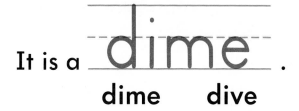

It is a ___dime___ .

dime   dive

1.

The girls have bikes.

They will go for a ___ride___ .

ripe   ride

2.

She got a fish.

The fish is ___fine___ to eat.

file   fine

3.

The men are working.

The ___pipe___ is very big.

pipe   pile

Directions: Some words have the long **i** vowel sound, as in **ride.** Look at the sample. The picture names a long **i** word. Read the sentences and the words in bold print. Write the word that belongs in the sentence. Read the sentence again to check your word.

 Have pupils give oral sentences using the words that were not answers.

"Look Out!" pages 38–42
Decoding: **i** (kite)

29

This bird is a blue jay.

(yes)   no

1.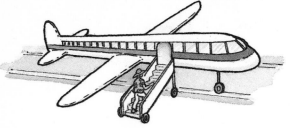

He will go on a train.

yes   (no)

2.

She will pay.

(yes)   no

3.

They are eating hay.

yes   (no)

4.

We are ready for rain.

yes   (no)

5.

She has a gray pail.

(yes)   no

Directions: Some words have the long **a** vowel sound. Each sentence on the page has a word with the long **a** vowel sound spelled **ai** as in **tail** or **ay** as in **stay**. Look at the picture in the sample. Read the sentence. Draw a line around **yes** or **no** to answer the question. Do the rest of the page the same way.

Have pupils fill in the blanks to make words that are not on this page: _____ **ay**, _____**ail**. Have pupils share their words to see how many different words they have written.

30   "Look Out!" pages 38–42
Decoding: <u>ai</u> (train), <u>ay</u> (play)

She has no balloon.   She wants one.

1. Mom fixed Kate's cut hand. Then she fixed the cake.

2. He went on a hike.   A snake bit him.

3. He is a teacher.   His class is going on a trip.

Directions: Sometimes you can tell what will happen next in a story. Read the two sentences in the sample. Look at the two pictures. Think about what will happen next. Draw a line around the picture that shows what happens next. Do the rest of the page the same way.

 Have pupils write a sentence and give it to a classmate to tell what might happen next.

"Look Out!" pages 38–42
Comprehension: predict outcomes

Let's
let's

Let's get a **big** pizza ___!___

for
_____

1. For _____ **my** friends ____

it
It is too hot ___!___

do
Do not eat it ___!___

On
_____

4. on _____ a **paper** mat ____

this
This pizza is **good** ___!___

Directions: A sentence tells a complete thought. It begins with a capital letter and ends with a punctuation mark. A sentence that shows excitement or surprise has an exclamation mark. Read the words in the sample. If the words make a sentence, write the first word. Then put an exclamation mark at the end of the sentence. If the words do not make a sentence, leave it blank. Do the rest of the page the same way.

 Have pupils write the non-sentences as sentences that show surprise and use the exclamation mark.

© D.C. Heath and Company

 **Write**

grandma   hair   his   lives   where

Carlos _____ lives _____ with his mom.

His grandma and
his Uncle Louie live on the same street.

Carlos likes to go to _____ his _____ grandma's

house. He likes the way she cuts his _____ hair _____ .

But Carlos likes the house _____ where _____
he lives the best.

Directions: Use some words from the story "Uncle Louie" to complete these sentences. Read the sentence in the sample. Read the words in bold print at the top of the page. Write the word that belongs in the sentence. Read the sentence again to check your word.

 Have pupils draw a line around all the words that name people on this page.

"Uncle Louie," pages 43–47
Vocabulary: key words

Name _____

Does Carlos tell his friends
about Uncle Louie?

yes

1. Do his friends know Uncle Louie?

no

2. Does Uncle Louie have a lot of hair?

no

3. Does Uncle Louie like to play
with his bear?

yes

4. Does Uncle Louie live
with Carlos's grandma?

yes

5. Does Uncle Louie read funny books?

no

Directions: This page asks questions about the story "Uncle Louie." Read the question in the sample and think about the
story. Write **yes** or **no** to answer the question. Do the rest of the page the same way.

 Have pupils discuss what they think Carlos's friends said when they saw Uncle Louie.

"Uncle Louie," pages 43–47
Selection Comprehension

 **Write**

aren't   didn't   hasn't
can't   doesn't   isn't

She <u>is not</u> running.

She ___*isn't*___ running.

1. She <u>can not</u> skate.

She ___*can't*___ skate.

2. He <u>does not</u> like to slide.

He ___*doesn't*___ like to slide.

3. He <u>has not</u> played ball.

He ___*hasn't*___ played ball.

4. They <u>are not</u> having fun.

They ___*aren't*___ having fun.

Directions: This page gives practice in contractions. Read the sentences in the sample. Read the words in bold print at the top of the page. Write the contraction that stands for the under lined words. Read the sentence again to check your word.

 Have pupils ask a question using two words that can be answered using a contraction at the top of the page. Other pupils respond to the question.

"Uncle Louie," pages 43–47
Decoding: contraction (verb + <u>not</u>)

1.

2.

3.

Directions: This page is about people, places, and things that go together. Look at the pictures in the first box of the sample. They are all things that go together. The second box shows places. Draw a line around the place where the things in the first picture belong. The last box shows people. Draw a line around the person who belongs in the first two pictures. Do the rest of the page the same way.

 Think about a place where you would like to be. Draw a picture of that place. Show some things and people who belong in that place.

What can I make for lunch __?__   ?   !

1. Will you mix this __?__   ?   !

2. That is a good white cake __!__   ?   !

3. Let's eat some of it __!__   ?   !

4. Do you like it __?__   ?   !

5. Thank you for cooking __!__   ?   !

Directions: A sentence that asks a question has a question mark. A sentence that shows excitement or surprise has an exclamation mark. Read the sentence in the sample. If it asks a question, put a question mark at the end. If it shows surprise, put an exclamation mark at the end. Do the rest of the page the same way.

 Have pupils write a question they might ask someone in their family.

"Uncle Louie," pages 43–47
Language: writing (question marks, exclamation marks)

bus   down   off   out   sat   stopped

Write

We took a ride on a ___bus___ .

My friends and I ___sat___ in the back.

The bus went ___down___ a big hill.

I looked ___out___ and saw some ducks.

The bus ___stopped___ .

We got ___off___ the bus. Now I can feed nuts to the ducks.

Directions: Use some words from the story "On the Bus" to complete these sentences. Read the sentence in the sample. Read the words in bold print at the top of the page. Write the word that belongs in the sentence. Read the sentence again to check your word.

Have pupils write this sentence, filling in the blank: **Squirrels love to eat ___** . They can draw a picture to go with their sentence.

"On the Bus" and "The Wheels on the Bus," pages 48–59
Vocabulary: key words

Draw a line under

Name _____

<u>Carlos, Kim, and Max</u>
<u>ran to the bus stop.</u>
Carlos, Kim, and Max
ran home.

1. Max got on the bus and sat with Kate.
<u>Max sat in the back of the big bus.</u>

2. <u>Big Ed sat with Kim.</u>
Big Ed sat with Max.

3. Big Ed said, "Have a nut."
<u>Big Ed said, "Your hat looks funny."</u>

4. Big Ed and Max ate lunch.
<u>Big Ed and Max ate nuts.</u>

5. <u>When the bus stopped, they were friends.</u>
Max helped Big Ed get off the bus.

Directions: This page tells about the story "On the Bus." Read the two sentences in the sample. Think about what happened in the story. Draw a line under the sentence that tells what happened. Do the rest of the page the same way.

Have pupils discuss what they think happened the next time Max saw Big Ed. Have pupils write a short conversation between them. Remind them to use quotation marks.

Write **be by go me so try Why**

"I want to ___go___ to my grandma's house."

"Will you come with ___me___ ?

We can go ___by___ bus."

"___Why___ do you want to go there?"

"My grandma is ___so___ nice. She will take

us to the pond. We can ___try___ to get a frog.

A frog will ___be___ a good pet."

Directions: Practice using words that have a long vowel sound at the end. Read the sentence in the sample. Read the words in bold print at the top of the page. Write the word that belongs in the sentence. Read the sentence again to check your word.

Have pupils write one sentence using these words: **we, sky, go.** Have pupils compare their sentences to see how many different ways they have used the words.

"On the Bus" and "The Wheels on the Bus," pages 48–59
Decoding: syllable patterns (CV)

 Write

hop   nap   pop   run   sit   win

The cows are ⟶ running .

1. The fox is _sitting_ .

2. The pig is _hopping_ .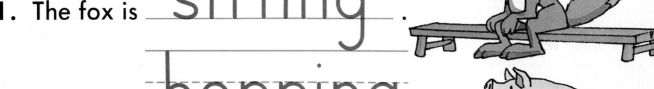

3. The snail is _winning_ .

4. The alligator is _napping_ .

5. The frog is _popping_ the balloon.

Directions: When **ing** is added to some words, like **tip** and **grin**, the consonant at the end of the word is doubled before the ending is added. Read the sentence in the sample. Read the words in bold print at the top of the page. Write the word that belongs in the sentence by adding **ing** to one of the words. Remember to double the final consonant. (Accept reasonable answers.)

 Have pupils write sentences using the words **stopping** and **getting.** Draw a line around the root word for each word.

"On the Bus" and "The Wheels on the Bus," pages 48–59
Decoding: spelling changes (doubled consonant before ending)

Pat loved his new red hat. He played in it.
He went to sleep in it too. But when he got up,
Pat's hat was not there.

Pat and his mom looked and looked for the hat. But
they did not see it. Then Pat's mom said, "Ask Dad."

"Dad!" said Pat. "Do you have my hat?"

"Yes," said his dad. "It helped me stay warm."

Then Pat's hat stayed on his head!

Why did Pat's mom look and look?

She wanted to get her hat back.

She was helping Pat look for his hat.

1. Why didn't Pat get mad at his dad?

He was glad to get his hat back.

His dad helped him look for the hat.

2. What is the best name for this story?

Pat's Hat

Pat's Mom Has a Hat

Directions: Think about the characters and what they did as you read the story. Read the question in the sample. Draw a
line under the correct answer. Do the rest of the page the same way.

 Have pupils tell how they know that Pat likes his hat. What are details in the story?

"On the Bus" and "The Wheels on the Bus," pages 48–59
Comprehension: character traits/plot

again   school   wished
jumped   tooth

Meg **wished** for her

tooth to come out.

When Meg came home from **school**,

she went to get some string.

Meg put the string on her **tooth**.

Then she **jumped**.

When Meg looked, the tooth was not out yet.

She jumped **again** and got her wish!

Directions: Use some words from the story "Not Yet" to complete these sentences. Read the sentence in the sample.
Read the words in the bold print at the top of the page. Write the word that belongs in the sentence. Read the sentence
again to check your word.

 Have pupils write "I Wish" at the top of their paper. Ask them to write three sentences
about their wish.

"Not Yet," pages 60–66
Vocabulary: key words

1.

2.

Rob ate a lot to make his tooth come out.

Meg's tooth came out.

3.

4.

5.

6.

7.

Dad said, "Go to sleep. That may help."

Rob said, "Oh, no! Here we go again."

Rob fell and his tooth came out.

Mom said, "Go out and play. That might help."

Meg said, "My tooth is out!"

Directions: This page tells about the story "Not Yet." Look at the sample and read the numbers and sentences. Draw a line from number **1** to the sentence that tells what happened first in the story. Draw a line from number **2** to the sentence that tells what happened second. Do the rest of the page the same way.

 Have pupils write a sentence telling how many teeth they have lost. Ask them to draw a picture of what they were doing when their teeth fell out.

"Not Yet," pages 60–66
Selection Comprehension

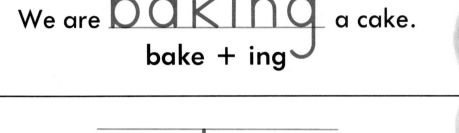

We are **baking** a cake.

bake + ing

1. She is **making** a dog balloon.

make + ing

2. Our friends are **coming**.

come + ing

3. They are **taking** some cake.

take + ing

4. We are all **having** fun.

have + ing

Directions: Some words end with an **e**, like **tape** and **love**. When **ing** is added to these words, the spelling of the root word changes. The final **e** is dropped. Read the sentence in the sample. Read the word in bold print. Add **ing** to the word and write it in the sentence. Remember to drop the final **e** before adding the ending. Read the sentence again to check your word. Do the rest of the page the same way.

 Have pupils write a sentence using **live + ing.**

"Not Yet," pages 60–66
Decoding: spelling changes (dropped -e before ending)

Name _____

foxes

fox

bus

1. buses

dish

2. dishes

box

3. boxes

dress

4. dresses

brush

5. brushes

lunch

6. lunches

Directions: Sometimes **es** is added to a word to mean more than one. Look at the picture in the sample. Write the word that means more than one. Do the rest of the page the same way.

 Have pupils write the plural forms of **wish** and **class.**

 **Write**

s   ed   ing

Jack is wishing for his tooth to come out.

I am **wishing** for my tooth to come out.
wish

1. I jumped up and down.

Jack is **jumping** too.
jump

2. I looked at my tooth.

Now Jack **looks** at his tooth.
look

3. Jack has waited for the tooth to come out.

I have **waited** too.
wait

Directions: Sometimes words have **s, ed,** or **ing** on the end. Read the sentences in the sample. Look at the word in bold print. Write the word in the sentence. Add **s, ed,** or **ing.** Read the sentence again.

 Have pupils write each word in bold print with the other endings.

"Not Yet," pages 60–66
Decoding: inflections -s, -ed, -ing

"Let's paint," said Stan.
"The paint is too thick.
We can not paint," said Len.
"Yes, we can," said Stan.
"I know how."

1. "I have a new pet," said Jill.
"It is very long and very thin."
"Is it a long dog?" asked Tom.
"No," said Jill. "My pet does
not have legs."

2. Dot said, "Let's have some fun.
Do you like the pond?"
"Yes, I do," said Jen.
Dot asked, "Do you like to eat
fish?"
"Yes," said Jen.
"Then come with me," Dot said.

Directions: Sometimes you can tell what will happen next in a story. Read the story in the sample. Think about what will happen next. Look at the pictures. Draw a line around the picture that shows what will happen next. Do the rest of the page the same way.

 Have pupils underline the clues in each story that helped them decide what would happen next.

"Not Yet," pages 60–66
Comprehension: predict outcomes

bulbs   grow   They

garden   plant   You'll

 Write

Dad and I wanted a **garden**.

We got some seeds and **bulbs**.

"Shall we **plant** the seeds and bulbs here?" asked Dad. "There is nothing here now."

"Yes," I said. "**They** will look

nice here. Will they **grow** soon?"

" **You'll** see," said Dad.

Directions: Use some words from the story "The Garden" to complete these sentences. Read the sentence in the sample. Read the words at the top of the page. Write the word that belongs in the sentence. Read the sentence again to check your word.

 Have pupils write a sentence about the new plants. Have them use the word **grew** in the sentence.

"The Garden" and "Maytime Magic," pages 67–75
Vocabulary: key words

49

Name _____

Mrs. Fine wanted to plant bulbs.

Mrs. Fine wanted to plant seeds.

1. Max had many bulbs at his home.

Max asked, "What are bulbs?"

2. Mrs. Fine said, "You'll see."

Mrs. Fine said, "The bulbs will be pretty."

3. Mrs. Fine planted the bulbs.

Mrs. Fine and the class planted the bulbs.

4. The bulbs grew in the garden.

The bulbs grew on a path.

5. When they grew, the plants looked very nice.

The class did not like the things that grew.

Directions: This page tells about the story "The Garden." Read the two sentences in the sample. Think about what happened in the story. Draw a line under the sentence that tells what happened. Do the rest of the page the same way.

 Have pupils imagine what the class did with the flowers they grew. Pupils can draw pictures showing their ideas. Then they can compare their different ideas.

50   "The Garden" and "Maytime Magic" pages 67–75
Selection Comprehension

Draw a line around

Name _____

My grandma likes to <u>zum</u> her day in the garden.

I <u>zum</u> my day with her there.

click (begin) love

1. Grandma can't <u>weth</u> very well.

I <u>weth</u> down and put seeds in for her.

(bend) melt wait

2. We plant big <u>glist</u> seeds.

One day Grandma will make a <u>glist</u> pie.

yellow grow (pumpkin)

3. When it <u>slonks</u>, we go inside.

The seeds get wet when it <u>slonks</u>.

tracks (rains) digs

4. Grandma says, "Do not <u>hoth</u> the little green plants."

"Wait and <u>hoth</u> them when they are big."

(pick) have help

Directions: Read the sentences in the sample. The underlined word is a nonsense word. It stands for a real word. Read the words in bold print. Draw a line around the word that belongs in both of the sentences in place of the nonsense word. Read the sentences again with your word.

 Have pupils make up two sentences with the same nonsense word in each one. Have pupils share their sentences orally and have classmates decide the real word.

"The Garden" and **"Maytime Magic,"** pages 67–75
Decoding: context

Jan and Fran planted some seeds.
They take care of the garden.
- ○ Seeds can not grow.
- ● New plants will grow.

1. Dad gets some paper and paints. He gets a brush.
- ● Dad will paint the pond and the ducks.
- ○ Dad will paint his house.

---

2. May wants a pet. Her mom doesn't like birds. Her dad doesn't like cats. May goes to a pet shop.
- ○ May will not get a pet.
- ● May will get a fish.

---

3. Grandma gets some cans. She gets the dog's dish and the cat's dish. Then she calls the dog and the cat.
- ○ Grandma will run with the dog and cat.
- ● The dog and cat will eat.

Directions: Sometimes you can tell what will happen next in a story. Look at the picture and read the story in the sample. Read the sentences . Fill in the circle beside the sentence that tells what will happen next. Do the rest of the page the same way.

 Have pupils tell what happened when May got home with her new pet.

"The Garden" and "Maytime Magic," pages 67–75
Comprehension: predict outcomes

Name _____

warm hands **hands**

1. a brown rabbit **rabbit**

2. the small shop **shop**

3. seeds grow **seeds**

4. Meg wished **Meg**

5. friends laugh **friends**

6. the teacher reads **teacher**

Directions: Some words name persons, places, and things. Read the words in the sample. Write the word that names something. Do the rest of the page the same way.

 Have pupils use any book in the classroom to find and write the names of people, places, and things.

"The Garden" and "Maytime Magic," pages 67–75
Language: writing (nouns)

 **Write**

from   grow   little   plants   tell   up

Kate put seeds and bulbs in her garden.

She likes to see the new  plants grow.

1.   The seeds and bulbs grow into

little plants.

2.   Kate sees the plants come  up .

Soon Kate picks them from her garden.

She will tell her grandma about them.

Directions: Use some words from the story "Seeds and Bulbs" to complete these sentences. Look at the sample and read the sentences. Read the words in bold print at the top of the page. Write the word that belongs in the sentence. Read the sentence again to check your word.

 Have pupils look through a seed catalog to find plants that grow from seeds and plants that grow from bulbs.

"Seeds and Bulbs," pages 76–79
Vocabulary: key words

Name _____

Do some plants grow from bulbs? **yes**

1. Are all bulbs big? **no**

2. Are all seeds little? **no**

3. Can a big plant grow from a little seed? **yes**

4. Do plants need many things to grow? **yes**

5. Does everything on a plant grow up? **no**

Directions: This page asks questions about the story "Seeds and Bulbs." Read the question in the sample. Think about the story. Write **yes** or **no** to answer the question. Do the rest of the page the same way.

Have pupils find out what the parts of a plant are called. Then they can draw a picture and label parts such as root, stem, leaf, and flower.

"Seeds and Bulbs," pages 76–79
Selection Comprehension

55

There is a drish in my garden.
The birds sit on the drish and sing.
brick   drum   (fence)

1. Plants grow in the rafe.
   The rafe is a warm time of year.
   (spring)   rain   rest

2. The plants all have suts.
   Some suts are thin and green.
   sand   sun   (stems)

3. The sun pligs on nice days.
   It pligs on a plant and makes it grow.
   rains   (shines)   sings

4. A crig is like a big glass.
   Some plants can look nice in a crig.
   (vase)   kite   crop

Directions: Read the sentences in the sample. The underlined word is a nonsense word. It stands for a real word. Read the words in bold print. One word will fit in both sentences in place of the nonsense word. Draw a line around the word that belongs in both sentences. Read the sentences again with your word.

 Have pupils use two of the words they chose in new sentences.

Draw a line under

You did a <u>nice</u> job.

new   funny   <u>goo</u>d

1. Our cat likes to <u>nap</u> in the sun.

     sit   <u>sleep</u>   run

2. He will <u>grab</u> the snake.

     <u>ge</u>t   see   read

3. You must <u>wait</u> here.

     go   <u>stay</u>   cook

4. I feel <u>fine</u> today.

     sick   <u>well</u>   sad

5. I want a <u>little</u> dog.

     <u>smal</u>l   big   new

Directions: Some words have meanings that are the same or almost the same as other words. Read the sentence in the sample. Read the words in bold print. Draw a line under the word that means the same or almost the same as the underlined word.

 Have pupils think of other words and their synonyms.

"Seeds and Bulbs," pages 76–79
Vocabulary: synonyms

We saw a big yellow bus. It had a blue flag.

1. We saw a big horse running.
No one was riding it.

2. We saw a green frog and red bugs sitting
on a big rock.

3. We saw a big yellow duck and five little ducks
in a pond.

Directions: These sentences tell about real things. Read the sentence in the sample. Think about the facts the sentence tells you. Look at the pictures. Draw a line around the picture that shows what the sentence tells about.

 Have pupils draw a picture of an animal and write a sentence about it on another piece of paper. Have other pupils match the pictures and the sentences.

"Seeds and Bulbs," pages 76–79
Comprehension: main idea/details

bugs   get   rocks
Everyone   liked   show

Write

"It's time for the ___show___ ," said Rob.

___Everyone___ will have fun.

Rob had a box with 2 big ___rocks___ in it.

There were some little ___bugs___ under the rocks.

"I ___get___ it—bug houses!" said Kate.

We all ___liked___ Rob's Show and Tell.

Directions: Use some words from the story "Show and Tell" to complete these sentences. Read the sentence in the sample. Read the words in bold print at the top of the page. Write the word that belongs in the sentence. Read the sentence again to check your word.

 Have pupils finish these sentences: **Today I liked** _____ . **I showed** _____ .

"Show and Tell," pages 90–96
Vocabulary: key words

59

✔   Mrs. Fine said it was time for Show and Tell.

✔   **1.** Meg showed a book at Show and Tell.

_____ **2.** Some of the class didn't like the book.

✔   **3.** Max showed a funny hat.

✔   **4.** Kate showed some rocks.

_____ **5.** Everyone liked Rob's bugs.

✔   **6.** Kim showed many friends.

Directions: This page tells about the story "Show and Tell." Look at the picture and read the sentence in the sample. If the sentence tells something that happened in the story, put a check on the line. If the sentence does not tell what happened in the story, leave the line blank. Do the rest of the page the same way.

 Have pupils draw a picture of something they would like to show during Show and Tell and write one thing they would tell about it.

bag   bug   fox   mop   pen

box   cat   hen   pan   pig

 Write

 This ___cat___ has a ___box___ .

1. This ___pig___ has a ___pen___ .

2. This ___fox___ has a ___pan___ .

3. This ___bug___ has a ___mop___ .

4. This ___hen___ has a ___bag___ .

Directions: Some words have short vowel sounds: **a** as in **cat, e** as in **ten, i** as in **pig, o** as in **pot,** or **u** as in **bug.** Read the words at the top of the page. Look at the picture in the sample. Read the sentence. Write the words that belong in the sentence. Read the sentence again to check your words.

Have pupils draw a picture to go with this sentence. **Ten men sat on a big red bug.** Then have them write the sentence under the picture.

"Show and Tell," pages 90–96
Decoding: short vowels a, e, i, o, u

61

Draw a
line
under

Name _____

The frog eats a bug.
The log runs into the pond.

1. The frog smiles and waves his hand.

2. "Hello, how are you?" the bugs ask the man.

3. The frog jumps into the pond.

4. The man looks at the duck.

5. The duck says, "Quack, quack."

6. The duck drives a big bus.

7. The man says, "Everything looks so nice here."

8 The plants say, " We want you to stay."

Directions: Some stories tell about things that could really happen. Other stories tell about make-believe things. Read the sentences in the sample. Draw a line under the sentence that tells about something that could **not** really happen. Do the rest of the page the same way.

 Have pupils change the underlined sentences to tell something that could really happen.

"Show and Tell," pages 90–96
Comprehension: reality–fantasy

Max the Cook

Max the Fox liked to cook.

He made green pizza and rock cake.

"Max is not a good cook," said his friends Kate the Cow and Ed the Pig.

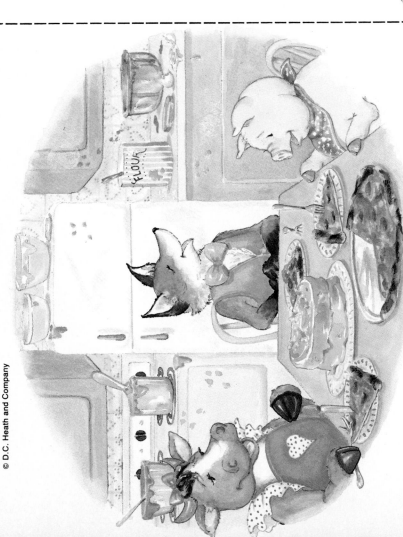

The next day Kate and Ed went to Max's house.

"Lunch is ready," said Max.

"The book helped me cook. I made rock pizza and green cake!"

"Oh!" said Kate and Ed.

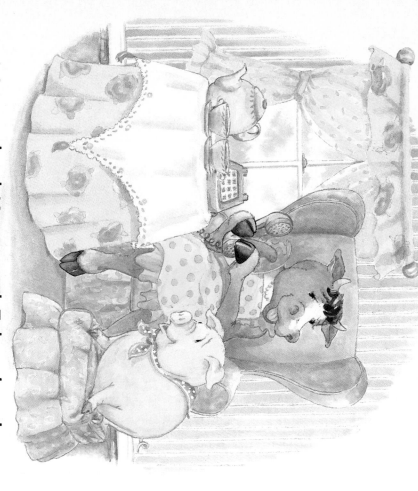

Max asked Kate and Ed to lunch.

They did not want to go.

"Max is not a good cook," said Ed.

"I know what we can do," said Kate.

"We can give Max a book to help him cook."

Kate and Ed went to Max's house.

"We have a book for you," said Kate.

"Oh good!" said Max.